Bob

Dot

Eco Apes Use Rubbish

Written by
Greg Cook

Illustrated by
Mark Chambers

Ragbag had a lot of rubbish.
"I like rubbish!" said Ragbag.

3

"This tub will be a ship,"
said Ragbag.

"I like this ship," said Bob.

"This tin and this cup will be a rocket," said Ragbag.

"I like this rocket!" said Dot.

"This box will be a hat,"
said Ragbag.

"Will it?" said Dot and Bob.

"This ship is for you Bob,"
said Ragbag.

"This rocket is for you Dot."

"This hat is for me!"